ALBERT
CAMUS

SUMMER

PENGUIN BOOKS

PENGUIN BOOKS

Published by the Penguin Group. Penguin Books Ltd, 27 Wrights Lane, London w8 5TZ, England. Penguin Books USA Inc., 375 Hudson Street, New York, New York 10014, USA. Penguin Books Australia Ltd, Ringwood, Victoria, Australia. Penguin Books Canada Ltd, 10 Alcorn Avenue, Toronto, Ontario, Canada M4V 3B2. Penguin Books (NZ) Ltd, 182–190 Wairau Road, Auckland 10, New Zealand · Penguin Books Ltd, Registered Offices: Harmondsworth, Middlesex, England · **These essays appear in** *Selected Essays and Notebooks* **by Albert Camus, edited and translated by Philip Thody and published by Penguin Books in 1970.** This edition published 1995 · Copyright 1954 by Editions Gallimard. Translation copyright © Hamish Hamilton and Alfred A. Knopf, Inc., 1967. Introduction, notes and selection © Philip Thody, 1970. All rights reserved · Typeset by Datix International Limited, Bungay, Suffolk. Printed in England by Clays Ltd, St Ives plc · Except in the United States of America, this book is sold subject to the condition that it shall not, by way of trade or otherwise, be lent, re-sold, hired out, or otherwise circulated without the publisher's prior consent in any form of binding or cover other than that in which it is published and without a similar condition including this condition being imposed on the subsequent purchaser · 10 9 8 7 6 5 4 3 2 1

CONTENTS

But you are born
For a limpid day   .
                    Hölderlin

Minotaur or the Halt at Oran

to Pierre Galindo

There are no more deserts, there are no more islands. Yet the need for them makes itself felt. If we are to understand the world, we must turn aside from it; if we are to serve men better, we must briefly hold them at a distance. But where can we find the solitude necessary to strength, the long breathing-space in which the mind can gather itself together and courage take stock of itself? We still have large towns. But these must fulfil certain conditions.

The cities that Europe can offer are too full of rumours from the past. A practised ear can still detect the rustling of wings, the quivering of souls. We feel the dizziness of centuries, of glory and of revolutions. There, we remember the clamour in which Europe was forged. There is not enough silence.

Paris is often a desert for the heart, but sometimes, as we stand looking over it from the Père–Lachaise, a wind of revolution suddenly fills this desert with flags and vanquished grandeurs. This same is true of certain Spanish towns, of Florence or of Prague. Salzburg would be peaceful without Mozart. But, from time to time, there runs across the Salzach the great cry of Don Juan plunging into hell. Vienna seems more silent, a maiden among cities. The stones there are no more than three centuries old, and their youth has known no sadness. But Vienna stands at a crossroads of history. The clash of empires rings round about her. On certain evenings, when the sky veils itself in blood, the stone horses on the monuments of the Ring seem about to take flight. In this fleeting moment, when everything tells of power and history, you can distinctly hear the Ottoman empire crashing under the charge of the Polish cavalry squadrons. Here, likewise, there is not enough silence.

It is, without doubt, this well-peopled solitude which men come to seek in the towns of Europe. Men who know the task awaiting them, that is. Here they can choose their company, take it and leave it. How many minds have been tempered by that walk between their hotel room and the old stones of the Île Saint-Louis! It is true that others have died there of loneliness. But it was there, in any case, that those who survived learned why they should grow and assert themselves. They were alone and yet not alone. Centuries of history and beauty, the burning evidence of a thousand past lives, walked with them along the Seine, and spoke to them both of traditions and of conquests. But their youth urged them to summon up this company. There comes a time, there come times in history, when such company is a crowd. 'It's between us two now,' exclaims Rastignac as he confronts the vast mouldering heap of the town of Paris. Yes, but two can be a crowd as well!

Deserts themselves have taken on meaning, have been overladen with poetry. They have become sacred places for all the sufferings of this world. But what the heart requires at certain moments is, on the contrary, a place without poetry. Descartes, for his meditations, chooses his desert: the busiest commercial city of his time. There he finds his loneliness, and the chance to write what is perhaps the greatest of our virile poems: 'The first [precept] was never to accept anything as true unless I knew without the slightest doubt that it was so.' One can have less ambition and yet the same nostalgia. But in the last three centuries Amsterdam has been covered with museums. To escape from poetry and rediscover the peacefulness of stones, we need other deserts, and other places with neither souls nor resting places. Oran is one of these.

THE STREET

I have often heard people from Oran complaining about their town: 'There is no interesting society here.' But you wouldn't want one if there were! A number of high-minded people have tried to acclimatize the customs of another world to this desert, faithful to the principle that no one can be of genuine service to art or to ideas without cooperation from others.* The result has been that the only instructive society is that of poker-players, boxing enthusiasts, bowling fanatics and regional societies. There, at least, the atmosphere is natural. After all, there is a certain kind of greatness which does not lend itself to elevation. It is infertile by nature. And anyone who wants to find it leaves interesting society behind him and goes down into the street.

The streets of Oran are abandoned to dust, pebbles and heat. If it rains, there is a flood and a sea of mud. But rain or shine, the shops have the same absurd and extravagant air. All the bad taste of Europe and the East has chosen Oran as its meeting place. There, piled on top of one another, you find marble greyhounds, swan-lake ballet dancers, Diana the Huntress in green galalith, discus-throwers and harvesters, everything that serves for wedding or birthday presents, the whole depressing population which a commercial and joking genie ceaselessly summons to our chimney-pieces. But this perseverance in bad taste here assumes a baroque extravagance where all can be forgiven. Behold, in a jewel-case of dust, the contents of one shop-window: ghastly plaster-cast models of tortured feet, a batch of Rembrandt sketches 'given away at 150 francs each', a quantity of 'practical jokes and tricks',

* In Oran, you meet Gogol's Klestakoff. He yawns and then: 'I 4 feel that we shall have to concern ourselves with higher things.'

tricolour wallets, an eighteenth-century pastel drawing, a mechanical plush donkey, bottles of *eau de Provence* for preserving green olives, and an ignoble-looking wooden virgin with an indecent smile. (So that no one shall remain ignorant, the 'management' has placed a label at its feet: 'Wooden virgin'.)

You can find in Oran:

1. Cafés whose grease-covered counters are strewn with the feet and wings of flies, where the proprietor never stops smiling although the place is always empty. A 'small black' used to cost twelve sous and a 'large one' eighteen;

2. Photographers' shops where the technique has not progressed since the invention of sensitized paper. They display a singular fauna, never encountered in the street, which ranges from the pseudo-sailor leaning with one elbow on a console-table, to the marriageable maiden, dress belted at the waist, standing with dangling arms against a sylvan scene. It can be assumed that these are not copies from nature but original creations;

3. An edifying plethora of undertakers. This is not because people die more frequently in Oran, but simply because, I suppose, they make more fuss about it.

The endearing simplicity of this nation of shop-keepers extends even to their advertisements. The future programme of a cinema in Oran gives details of a third-class film. I note the adjectives 'magnificent', 'splendid', 'extraordinary', 'marvellous', 'overwhelming' and 'stupendous'. To conclude, the management informs the public of the considerable sacrifices it has had to make in order to be able to present this astonishing 'production'. However, the price of the seats will remain the same.

It would be wrong to think that this merely shows the taste for exaggeration peculiar to Mediterranean countries. What the authors of this miraculous prospectus are really doing is giving proof of their psychological perspicacity. They need to overcome the indifference and deep apathy which men feel in this country as soon as they have to choose between two entertainments, two jobs, and even, quite frequently, between two women. You decide only when compelled to do so. And the advertisers are perfectly aware of this. They will go to the same extremes as in America, having the same reasons for exasperation in both places.

Finally, the streets of Oran tell us about the two essential pleasures of the local youth: having its shoes shone, and parading these same shoes along the boulevard. To gain a correct idea of the first of these two delights, you must entrust your shoes at ten o'clock on a Sunday morning to the shoe-shiners of the Boulevard Gallieni. There, perched on a high stool, you can enjoy that peculiar satisfaction which even the profane can receive from the spectacle of men as deeply and visibly in love with their work as are the shoe-cleaners of Oran. Everything is worked out to the last detail. Several brushes, three kinds of polishing rag, shoe-polish mixed with petrol: one might believe that the operation has been concluded when a perfect shine comes to birth beneath the application of the soft brush. But the same eager hand puts a second coat of polish on the gleaming surface, rubs it, dulls it, drives the cream into the very heart of the leather and then brings out, with the same brush, a double and truly definitive shine which emerges from the innermost depths.

The marvels thus obtained are then exhibited to the connoisseurs. Really to appreciate the pleasures offered by the boulevard, you must attend the fancy-dress dances organized by the youth of Oran every evening in the town's main thoroughfares. Between the ages of sixteen and twenty, in fact, the 'fashionable' young Oranais choose to model their elegance on the American cinema and disguise themselves before going to dine. With curly brilliantined hair flowing from under a felt hat which is cocked over the left ear while its brim obliterates the right eye, neck encircled in a collar generous enough to receive the continuation of the hair, the microscopic knot of the tie held in place by the strictest of pins, jacket hanging half-way down the thighs and nipped in at the hips, light-coloured trousers hanging short, shoes gleaming above triple soles, these youths parade along the pavement their unshakeable self-confidence and the steel tips of their shoes. They attempt to imitate, in all matters, the gait, the self-confidence and superiority of Mr Clark Gable.

Consequently, the more critically minded members of the town normally baptize these young men, by the grace of unaffected pronunciation, 'Clarques'.

However that may be, the main boulevards of Oran are invaded late every afternoon by an army of agreeable adolescents who take the greatest pains to look like gangsters. Since the young girls of Oran know that they have been destined since birth to marry these tender-hearted rogues, they also flaunt the make-up and elegance of the great American actresses. The same cynics consequently christen them 'Marlenes'. Thus when on the evening boulevards the chirping of birds rises from the palm-trees to the sky, scores of Clarques and Marlenes meet, casting appreciative and evaluating glances, happy to live and to appear, absorbed for an hour in the bliss of perfect existences. What we then behold, in the words of the jealous, are the meetings of the American commission. But these words reveal the bitterness of the over-thirties who have no part in such games. They fail to recognize these daily congresses of youth and romantic love for what they are – the parliaments of birds found in Hindu literature. But no one on the boulevards of Oran discusses the Problem of Being, or is concerned with the way to perfection. All that remains is the fluttering of wings, the flaunting of outspread tails, flirtations between victorious graces, all the rapture of a careless song that fades with the coming of night.

I can already hear Klestakoff saying: 'We must concern ourselves with higher things.' Alas, he is quite capable of doing so. A little encouragement, and in a few years' time he will people this desert. But, for the time being, a gently secretive soul can find rest in this facile town, with its parade of made-up maidens who have no disguise for feelings, who make so poor a pretence at coquetry that we immediately see through their wiles. Concern ourselves with the higher life! We should do better to use our eyes: Santa Cruz carved out of the rock, the mountains, the flat sea, the violent wind and the sun, the tall cranes in the docks, the sheds, the quays and the gigantic flights of stairs which scale the rock on which the town is set, and in the town itself these games and this boredom, this tumult and this solitude. Perhaps none of this is high enough. But the great value of these overpopulated islands is that in them the heart can strip itself bare. Silence is now possible only in noisy towns. From Amsterdam Descartes wrote to Balzac, now old, 'Each day I stroll through the confusion of a great people, with as much freedom and quiet as you find in your lanes.'

THE DESERT IN ORAN

Compelled to live in the presence of an admirable land-scape, the Oranais have overcome this formidable trial by screening themselves behind extremely ugly buildings. You expect a town opening out on to the sea, washed and refreshed by the evening breeze. And, except for the Spanish district, you find a city which has its back to the sea, which has been built turning in upon itself, like a snail. Oran is a long, circular yellow wall topped with a hard sky. At first, men wander round the labyrinth, looking for the sea as for Ariadne's thread. But they turn round and round in the yellow, stifling streets until, in the end, the Oranais are devoured by the Minotaur of boredom. The Oranais have long since ceased wandering. They let the monster eat them.

No one can know what stone really is until he has been to Oran. In this dustiest of cities the pebble is king. It is so well loved that merchants display it in their windows, either as a paperweight or simply for its appearance. People pile them up along the streets, doubtless for pure visual pleasure, since a year later the pile is still there. Things which elsewhere derive their poetry from being green here take on a face of stone. The hundred or so trees which can be found in the business quarter of the town have been carefully covered over with dust. They have become trees from a petrified forest, their branches exuding an acrid, dusty smell. In Algiers the Arab cemeteries have their well-known gentleness. In Oran above the Ras-el-Aïn ravine, facing the sea for once, what you see laid out against the blue sky are fields of chalky, crumbly pebbles set blindingly on fire by the sun. In the midst these dead bones of the earth, scattered patches of crimson geraniums give the landscape its life and fresh blood. The whole town is held fast in a clamp of stone. Seen from the Planters, the cliffs which hold it in their grip are so thick that the landscape loses its reality between the stone. Man is an outlaw. So much heavy beauty seems to come from another world.

If what we call a desert is a place without a soul in which the sky alone is king, then Oran awaits its prophets. All around and above the town the brutal nature of Africa is, in fact, resplendent in its most burning glory. It splits open the ill-chosen décor which men have laid upon it, utters its violent cries between each house and over all the housetops. If you go up on to one of the roads running along the side of the Santa Cruz mountain, what you see first of all are the scattered and brightly coloured blocks of Oran. But as soon as you go a little higher, the jagged cliffs surrounding the plateau seem to be crouching in the sea like red beasts. From higher still, great whirlpools of sun and wind swirl over the untidy town, blowing and battering through it as it lies scattered in confusion over all four corners of the rocky landscape. You see the clash between the magnificent anarchy of men and the permanence of an unchanging sea. This gives the road along the mountain-side an overwhelming scent of life.

Deserts have something implacable about them. The

mineral sky of Oran, its trees and streets in their layer of dust, all join forces to create this thick and impassive world in which the mind and heart cannot be turned from themselves, nor from their one subject, which is man. Here I am speaking of harsh refuges. People write books about Florence and Athens. These towns have formed so many European minds that they must have a meaning. They keep the power to sadden or excite. They calm a certain hunger of the soul whose proper food is memory. But how can one feel tender in a town where nothing appeals to the mind, where ugliness itself is anonymous, where the past is reduced to nothingness? What can be the attraction of emptiness, of boredom, of an indifferent sky? Solitude, without a doubt, and perhaps human beings as well. There is a certain race of men for whom human beings, wherever they are beautiful, make up a bitter homeland. Oran is one of the thousand capitals such men possess.

SPORT

The Central Sporting Club in the Rue du Fondouk in Oran is presenting an evening of boxing which it proclaims will be appreciated by those who really love the sport. What this actually means is that the boxers whose names are on the posters are far from being champions, that some of them will be stepping into the ring for the first time, and that you can therefore count on the courage if not on the skill of the contestants. An Oranais having electrified me by the formal undertaking that 'blood will flow', I find myself this evening among the real lovers of the sport.

It would appear that the latter never demand comfort. A ring has in fact been erected at the far end of a kind of whitewashed, garishly-lit garage with a corrugated iron roof. Folding chairs have been set up on all four sides of the ropes. These are the 'ring-side seats'. Other seats have been set up in the body of the hall, and at the far end there is a wide-open space known as the 'free area', so named because not one of the five hundred people standing there can take out his pocket handkerchief without causing a serious accident. This rectangular box contains a thousand men and two or three women – of the type who, according to my neighbour, 'always want to show off'. Everyone is sweating ferociously. While we wait for the 'white hopes' to step into the ring, an immense loudspeaker grinds out Tino Rossi. Ballads before butchery.

The true lovers of the sport possess limitless patience. The fights promised for nine o'clock have not yet started at half-past, and yet no one complains. It is a warm spring evening, and the smell of humanity in its shirt-sleeves is intoxicating. Violent discussions are accompanied by the 13 periodic popping of lemonade bottle corks and the tireless lamentations of the Corsican singer. A few new arrivals are fitted in, when a projector casts a blinding light on to the ring. The white hopes step into the ring.

These white hopes, or beginners, who fight for pleasure, are always anxious to prove it by massacring each other at the first opportunity, with a fine disregard for technique. None of them has ever lasted more than three rounds. The hero of the evening in this respect is a certain 'Aero the Kid' who normally sells lottery tickets on café terraces. His opponent, in fact, has taken an unlucky dive out of the ring at the beginning of the second round under the impact of a fist that whirled like a propeller.

The crowd has grown a little more excited, but still out of politeness. It takes deep, grave breaths of the sacred odour of embrocation. It contemplates this series of slow rites and confused sacrifices which are made even more authentic by the propitiatory patterns cast by the struggling shadows on the whiteness of the wall. These are the formal prologue of a savage and calculated religion. The trance will come only later.

And, at this very moment, the loudspeaker introduces Amar, 'the tough Oranais who never gives up', against Pérez, 'the Algerian puncher'. The profane might well misinterpret the howls which greet the presentation of the boxers in the ring. They might think that this was some sensational fight in which the two rivals were going to settle a personal quarrel known to the public. It is indeed a quarrel that they are going to settle, but one that for the last hundred years has cast a mortal division between Algiers and Oran. A few hundred years ago, these two North African towns would have already bled each other white, as Florence and Pisa did in happier times. Their rivalry is all the stronger from being based on absolutely nothing. Having every reason to love each other, their hatred is all the fiercer. The Oranais accuse the Algerians of being 'stuck-up'. The Algerians insinuate that the Oranais are ill-bred. These are bloodier insults than one might think, since they are metaphysical. And because they cannot besiege each other, Oran and Algiers meet, struggle and exchange insults in the field of sport, statistics and public works.

It is consequently a page of history that is unfolding itself in the ring. And the tough Oranais, supported by a thousand howling voices, is defending against Pérez a way of life and the pride of a province. Truth compels me to say that Amar is putting his points badly. His arguments arc out of order: he lacks reach. The Algerian puncher, on the other hand, is long enough in the arm and makes his points persuasively on his opponent's eyebrow. The Oranais bears his colours triumphantly, amidst the howls of the frenzied spectators. In spite of repeated encouragement from the gallery and from my neighbour, in spite of the fearless 'Bash him', 'Give him what for', the insidious cries of 'Foul', 'Oh, the ref. never saw him', the optimistic 'He's shagged', 'He's had it', the Algerian is declared winner on points to the accompaniment of interminable booing. My neighbour, who likes to talk about the sporting spirit, applauds ostentatiously, whispering to me meanwhile in a voice made hoarse by so much shouting, 'Like this, they won't be able to say down *there* that the Oranais are savages.'

But in the body of the hall a number of fights that were unlisted on the programme have already broken out. Chairs are waved in the air, the police force their way through, the excitement is at its height. To calm these good people and contribute to the restoration of silence, the 'management' instantly entrusts the loudspeaker with the thunderous march of *Sambre-et-Meuse*. For a few moments the hall takes on a wondrous aspect. Confused bunches of fighters and indulgent referees wave to and fro beneath the policemen's grasp, the gallery is delighted and urges them to further efforts with wild cries, cock-a-doodle-doos or ironic mewing, soon submerged in the irresistible flood of military music.

But the announcement that the main fight is about to start is sufficient to restore calm. This happens quickly with no flourishes, as when actors leave the stage as soon as the play is over. In the most natural way in the world hats are dusted, chairs put back in their place, and every face immediately assumes the benign expression of the respectable spectator who has paid for his seat at a family concert.

The last fight of the evening confronts a French naval champion with an Oranais boxer. This time, it is the latter who has the advantage of reach. But during the initial rounds his advantage makes little appeal to the crowd. It is digesting its excitement, convalescing. It is still short of breath. Its catcalls lack animosity. If it applauds, it is with no vigour. The spectators split into two camps, as they must do if order is to prevail. But each man's choice is guided by that indifference which succeeds great weariness. If the Frenchman holds on in the clinches, if the Oranais forgets that one does not attack with the head, the boxer is bowled over by a broadside of hisses but immediately put back on his feet by a salvo of applause. It is not until the seventh round that sport comes back to the surface, accompanied by the emergence from their fatigue of its true lovers. The Frenchman, in fact, has been put down on the canvas, and, anxious to win back points, has charged at his opponent. 'Here we go,' says my neighbour. 'This will be murder.' And, in fact, that is what it is. Covered in sweat beneath the implacable lights, the two boxers open their guard, close their eyes and swing. They push with their knees and shoulders, exchange their blood and snort with fury. Instantaneously the spectators stand erect and punctuate each hero's effort with their cries. They receive the blows, return them, swell them by a thousand harsh and panting voices. The same men who had chosen their favourite in indifference stick to their choice through obstinacy and endow it with passion. Every ten seconds my right ear is pierced by a shout from my neighbour 'Go on, bluejacket! Bash him, matelot', while a spectator in front of us shouts '¡Anda, hombre!' to the Oranais. The hombre and the bluejacket comply, escorted, in this whitewashed temple of cement and corrugated iron, by a crowd in frenzied worship of these low-browed gods. The dull thud of every blow echoes in enormous vibrations through the very body of the crowd, which gasps its last breath with the boxers themselves.

In this atmosphere the announcement of a draw is badly received. It runs contrary to what, in the crowd, is an utterly Manichean vision: there is good and evil, the victor and the vanquished. One is either right or wrong. The conclusion of this impeccable logic is immediately provided by two thousand energetic lungs which accuse the judges of being either bought or sold. But the bluejacket has gone to embrace his opponent in the ring and drinks his fraternal sweat. This is enough to make the crowd effect an immediate volte-face and explode in applause. My neighbour is right: they are not savages.

The crowd which now flows out beneath a sky filled with silence and with stars has just fought the most exhausting of battles. It says nothing, fades furtively away, too exhausted for exegesis. There is good and evil, this religion is merciless. The cohort of the faithful is now nothing more than a gathering of black and white shadows disappearing into the night. The reason is that strength and violence are lonely gods. They give nothing to the memory. On the contrary, they scatter miracles by handfuls in the present. They are on the same scale as this people which lacks a past and celebrates its communions round boxing rings. They are slightly difficult rites, but which simplify everything. Good and evil, the victor and the vanquished: at Corinth two temples stood side by side, the one of Violence, the other of Necessity.

MONUMENTS

For many reasons connected as much with economy as with metaphysics, one can say that Oranais style, if such a thing exists, finds clear and powerful expression in that singular edifice known as the *Maison du Colon*. Oran has, indeed, no lack of monuments. The town has its quota of Imperial Marshals, and of ministers and local benefactors. You come across them in little dusty squares, resigned to rain as to sun, converted like everything else to stone and boredom. But they nevertheless represent something imported. In this happy barbarity they stand as regrettable traces of civilization.

Oran, on the contrary, has erected altars and rostrums 19

to itself. When the Oranais had to construct a building to be shared by the innumerable agricultural organizations which provide the country with its livelihood, they decided to erect, using the most solid materials, and placing it at the centre of their business city, a convincing representation of their virtues: *La Maison du Colon.* To judge by this building, these virtues are three in number: boldness of taste, love of violence, and a sense of historical synthesis. Egypt, Byzantium and Munich have collaborated in the delicate construction of a pastry-cake representing an immense inverted cup. Multicoloured stones, of the most startling effect, have been set along each side of the roof. The brightness of these mosaics is so persuasive that all one can discern at first is a shapeless dazzle. But on closer inspection they do reveal their meaning to the fully awakened attention: a gracious settler, wearing a bow tie and a solar topee, is receiving the homage of a procession of slaves clad as nature intended.* Finally, the edifice has been erected, with all its illuminations, at the centre of a crossroads, amid the bustle of the tiny gondola-shaped tramways whose squalor is one of the charms of the town.

Oran is, moreover, very attached to the two lions which stand on its main square. Since 1888 they have sat majestically on either side of the staircase leading up to the town

* Another of the qualities of the Algerian race is, as can be seen, frankness.

hall. Their creator was called Cain. They look majestic and are short in the body. It is said that, at night, they descend one after the other from their pedestal and pad silently round the darkened square, stopping on occasion to urinate at length between the tall dusty fig-trees. These are, naturally, rumours to which the Oranais lend an indulgent ear. But it is unlikely.

In spite of some researches I have not been able to develop any great enthusiasm for Cain. All I have discovered is that he enjoyed the reputation of a skilful depicter of animals. Nevertheless, I often think about him. This is a tendency which the mind acquires in Oran. Here is a sonorously named artist who gave this town a work of no importance. Several hundred thousand men have grown familiar with the jovial lords of the jungle that he placed in front of a pretentious town hall. It is one kind of artistic success. These lions doubtless bear witness, as do thousands of other works of the same kind, to something very different from talent. Men have painted *The Night Watch*, *Saint Francis Receiving the Stigmata*, *The Exaltation of the Flower*, or carved the statue of David. What Cain did was erect two grinning felines in the town square of a trading province overseas. But one day the statue of David will crumble into ruin with the town of Florence, and these lions will perhaps be saved from the disaster. Once again, they bear witness to something else.

Can I clarify this idea? These statues contain both

insignificance and solidity. The mind has made no contribution, and matter an enormously large one. Mediocrity seeks to endure by every means, including bronze. We refuse it the right to eternity, but it takes it every day. Is it not itself eternity? In any case, there is something moving in this perseverance, and it bears its lesson, which is the one offered by all the monuments of Oran and by Oran itself. For an hour a day, for once in a while, it compels you to take an interest in something which is not important. The mind can profit from such moments of calm. This is how it takes the cure and, since it must pass through these moments of humility, I feel that this opportunity to stultify itself is better than others. Everything perishable seeks to endure. Let us then admit that everything wishes to endure. The works of man have no other meaning, and in this respect Cain's lions have the same chance of succeeding as the ruins at Angkor. This encourages modesty.

There are other monuments in Oran. This, at least, is what we must call them, since they too bear witness for their town, in perhaps a more significant way. They are the excavations which, at the moment, cover the coastline over a distance of ten kilometres. The apparent aim is to transform the brightest of bays into an enormous port. In fact, it is yet another opportunity for man to pit himself against stone.

22   In the canvases of certain Flemish masters you see the

insistent recurrence of an admirably spacious theme: the construction of the Tower of Babel. You see immense landscapes, rocks reaching up into the sky, escarpments teeming with workmen, animals, ladders, strange machines, ropes and beams. Men, in fact, are in the picture only to bring out the inhuman vastness of the buildings. It is this that comes to your mind on the coast road running to the west of Oran.

There, clinging to immense slopes, are rails, tip-trucks, cranes, and miniature railways . . . Under a devouring sun toy-like locomotives circumnavigate vast blocks of stone to the accompaniment of whistles, dust and smoke. Night and day a nation of ants swarms over the smoking carcass of the mountain. Scores of men, hanging from the same rope against the cliff face, their bellies pressed to the handles of pneumatic drills, quiver day after day in mid-air, unloosing whole sections of stone that crash down in a roar of dust. Farther along, the trucks tip their load from the top of the slopes, and the rocks suddenly launched towards the sea roll and dive into the water, each heavy block followed by a shower of lighter stones. At regular intervals, at dead of night or in the middle of the day, explosions shake the whole mountain and lift up the sea itself.

What man is doing, in these excavations, is making a head-on attack against stone. And if we could for a moment forget the harsh slavery which makes this work possible, we should be filled with admiration. These stones, wrenched from the mountain, help man in his projects. They pile up beneath the first waves, gradually emerge, and finally take shape as a jetty that will soon be covered with men and machines moving daily farther out to sea. Vast steel jaws gnaw unceasingly at the cliff's belly, swivel round and disgorge their excess rubble into the sea. As the cliff face sinks lower, the whole coast pushes the sea relentlessly backwards.

Stone, of course, cannot be destroyed. All that can be done is move it around. Whatever happens, it will always outlast the men who use it. For the moment it lends itself to their determination to act. Even that determination is doubtless quite gratuitous. But it is man's task to move things around: he must choose between doing that or doing nothing at all.* Clearly, the Oranais have chosen. Before that indifferent bay, they will still go on for years piling up heaps of pebbles along the coast. In a hundred years, that is to say tomorrow, they will have to start again. But today these piles of rock bear witness for the men who wend their way among them, their faces set in a mask of dust and sweat. The true monuments of Oran remain its stones.

* This essay deals with a particular temptation. One must have experienced it. One can then choose to act or not to act, but with full awareness of what is involved.

It seems that the Oranais are like that friend of Flaubert who, on his deathbed, cast a last look at this irreplaceable earth and cried out: 'Close the window, it's too beautiful.' They have closed the window, they have walled themselves in, they have exorcized the landscape. But Le Poittevin is dead, and now that he is gone tomorrow has followed tomorrow. Similarly, beyond the yellow walls of Oran the earth and sea pursue their indifferent dialogue. This permanence which the world possesses has always held a contradictory charm for man. It inspires him and casts him into despair. The world never has more than one thing to say, it is interesting, then boring. But, in the long run, it conquers through obstinacy. It is always right.

As soon as you leave the gates of Oran, nature takes on a harsher note. Towards Canastel lie immense stretches of waste land, covered with scented bushwood. There, the wind and sun speak only of solitude. Above Oran stands the Santa Cruz mountain, with its plateau and the thousand ravines leading to it. Roads, along which in former times one could travel in a coach, cling to the hillsides overlooking the sea. In January some are covered in flowers. Buttercups and daisies turn them into sumptuous paths, woven with white and yellow. On Santa Cruz there is no more to be said. But if I had to speak of this 25 mountain, I should forget the sacred processions which climb its harsh slopes on the great feast days and evoke other pilgrimages. They travel in solitude through the red stone, rise above the motionless bay, before descending to consecrate a perfect and shining hour to frugality.

Oran also has its deserts of sand: its beaches. The ones near the city gates are empty only in winter and in spring. Then they are plateaux covered with asphodels and peopled with small bare villas among the flowers. The sea growls a little, lower down. But the sun, the slight wind, the whiteness of the asphodels, the harsh blue of the sky already foreshadow the summer and the golden youth which then covers the beach, long hours on the sand and the sudden gentleness of evening. Each year sees a new harvest of flower-maidens on these shores. Apparently, they last only for one season, since the following year other warm corollas take their place, who the previous summer were still little girls with bodies hard as buds. Coming down from the plateau at eleven in the morning, all this young flesh, scarcely covered by its motley garments, flows over the sand like a multicoloured wave.

One must go farther off (and strangely near, in fact, to that place where two hundred thousand men walk round in their own tracks) to find a landscape that is still untouched: long empty dunes on which the passage of men has left no trace but a worm-eaten hut. From time to time an Arab shepherd leads across the top of the dunes the black and beige stains made by his herd of goats. On these beaches in the province of Oran each summer morning feels like the first morning of the world. Each dusk feels like the last, a solemn death proclaimed at sunset by a final light which darkens every shade. The sea is ultramarine, the road the colour of dried blood, the beach yellow. Everything vanishes with the green sun; an hour later the dunes are flowing with moonlight. Then comes night, boundless beneath a shower of stars. Storms drift occasionally across the night, and flashes of lightning flow along the dunes, turn the sky pale, and cast an orange-coloured glow upon the sand or on our eyes.

But this cannot be shared through speech. It must be lived. So much solitude and grandeur give these places an unforgettable appearance. In the mild early dawn, beyond the small, still black and bitter waves, a new being cleaves the waters of night that are so heavy to bear. The memory of these joys gives me no regret, and this is how I know that they were good. After so many years, they are still there, somewhere in this heart which finds fidelity so hard. And I know that today, if I want to visit them, the same sky will still pour down its cargo of stars and breezes upon the deserted dunes. These are the lands of innocence.

But innocence needs sands and stones. And man has forgotten how to live with them. This, at least, appears to be the case, since he has shut himself up in this strange town of slumbering boredom. It is nevertheless this confrontation which gives Oran its value. The capital of boredom, besieged by innocence and beauty, is hemmed in by an army as rich in soldiers as in stones. Yet, at certain times, how tempted one feels in this town to pass over to the enemy! How tempted to merge oneself with these stones, to become indistinguishable from this burning and impassive universe which stands as a challenge to history and its agitations! A vain temptation, no doubt. But there is in every man a deep instinct which is neither that of destruction nor that of creation. It is simply the longing to resemble nothing. In the shade of the warm buildings of Oran, on its dusty asphalt, one sometimes hears this invitation. It seems that, for a time, the minds which yield to it are never disappointed. They find the shades of Eurydice and the sleep of Isis. These are the deserts where thought refills its lungs, the cool hand of evening on a troubled heart. No vigil can be kept upon this Mount of Olives; the mind joins and approves the sleeping Apostles. Were they really wrong? They did have their revelation after all.

Let us think of Sakia-Mouni in the desert. He spent long years there, crouching motionless and looking up to heaven. The gods themselves envied him this wisdom and this fate of stone. In his stiff and outstretched hands, the swallows had made their nest. But, one day, they flew away to follow the call of distant lands. And the man who had killed in himself desire and will, glory and sadness, began to weep. Thus it happens that flowers grow from the rock. Yes, let us consent to stone when we must. It too can give us the secret and the rapture that we seek in faces. Of course, this cannot last. But what is there that can? The face's secret fades, and we must tread once more the closed paths of desire. And if stone can do no more for us than can the human heart, it can at least do just as much.

'To be nothing!' For thousands of years this cry has inspired millions of men in revolt against desire and suffering. Its echoes have travelled all the way across centuries and oceans, before coming to rest upon the oldest sea in the world. They still echo softly against the solid cliffs of Oran. Everyone, in this country, follows this advice without knowing it. Naturally, it is practically in vain. Nothingness is no more in our grasp than is the absolute. But since we welcome as evidence of grace the eternal signs which roses or the sufferings of men can bring us, let us also not reject the rare invitations to sleep which are granted to us by the earth. The second have as much truth as the first.

This, perhaps, is the Ariadne's thread of this frenzied and sleepwalking town. We acquire the virtues, the wholly provisional virtues, of certain boredom. To be spared, we must say 'yes' to the Minotaur. It is an old and fecund wisdom. Above the sea, lying silent at the foot of the red cliffs, we need only to hold ourselves exactly balanced between the two massive headlands which, to right and left, stand bathed in the clear water. In the chugging of a coastguard vessel crawling out to sea, bathed in radiant light, you can now distinctly hear the stifled call of glittering and inhuman forces: it is the Minotaur's farewell.

It is midday, the day itself stands at a point of balance. His rite accomplished, the traveller receives the price of his deliverance: the little stone, dry and soft as an asphodel, that he picks up on the cliff. For the initiate the world is no heavier to carry than that stone. The burden of Atlas is easy; all you need do is choose your time. You then understand that for an hour, a month, a year, these shores can lend themselves to freedom. They offer the same uncritical welcome to the monk, the civil servant and the conqueror. There were days when I used to expect, in the streets of Oran, to meet Descartes or Cesare Borgia. This did not happen. But perhaps another will be more fortunate than I. A great action, a great undertaking, virile meditation required in days gone by the solitude of a desert or a convent. There men kept vigil over the weapons of their mind. Where better could we keep this vigil now than in the emptiness of a large town built to last in the midst of mindless beauty?

Here is the small stone, soft as an asphodel. It lies at the beginning of everything. Flowers, tears (if you insist), departures and struggles are for tomorrow. In the middle of the journey, when the heavens open their fountains of light in vast, resounding space, the headlands all along the coast look like a fleet of ships impatient to weigh anchor. These heavy galleons of rock and light lie trembling on their keels as if in preparation for a voyage to the islands of the sun. Oh, mornings in Oran! From high on the plateaux the swallows swoop down into the immense cauldrons of simmering air. The whole coast is ready for departure, a thrill of adventure runs along it. Tomorrow, perhaps, we shall set sail together.

1939

The Almond Trees

'Do you know,' Napoleon once said to Fontanes, 'what fills me most with wonder? The powerlessness of force to establish anything. There are only two powers in the world: the sword and the mind. In the end the sword is always conquered by the mind.'

Conquerors, we see, are sometimes melancholy. They must pay something for so much vainglory. But what, a hundred years ago, was true of the sword, is no longer true today for the tank. The conquerors have made progress, and the dismal silence of mindless places has established its long reign over a lacerated Europe. At the time of the hideous wars of Flanders Dutch painters could perhaps still paint the cockerels in their farmyards. The Hundred Years War has likewise been forgotten, and yet the prayers of the Silesian mystics still inhabit some men's hearts. But today things have changed, the painter and the monk are mobilized: we are one with this world. The mind has lost that regal certainty which a conqueror could acknowledge; it now exhausts itself in cursing force, for want of knowing how to master it.

There are noble souls who keep deploring this, and saying it is evil. We do not know if it is evil, but we know it is a fact. The conclusion is that we must come to terms with it. All we then need to know is what we want. And what indeed we want is never again to bow down before the sword, never more to declare force to be in the right when it is not serving the mind.

This, it is true, is an endless task. But we are here to pursue it. I do not have enough faith in reason to subscribe to a belief in progress, or to any philosophy of History. But I do at least believe that men have never ceased to grow in the knowledge of their destiny. We have not overcome our condition, and yet we know it better. We know that we live in contradiction, but that we must refuse this contradiction and do what is needed to reduce it. Our task as men is to find those few first principles that will calm the infinite anguish of free souls. We must stitch up what has been torn apart, render justice imaginable in the world which is so obviously unjust, make happiness meaningful for nations poisoned by the misery of this century. Naturally, it is a superhuman task. But tasks are called superhuman when men take a long time to complete them, that is all.

Let us then know our aims, standing steadfast on the mind, even if force dons the mask of ideas or of comfort to lure us from our task. The first thing is not to despair. Let us not listen too much to those who proclaim that the world is ending. Civilizations do not die so easily, and even if this world were to collapse, it will not have been the first. It is indeed true that we live in tragic times. But too many people confuse tragedy with despair. 'Tragedy', Lawrence said, 'ought to be a great kick at misery.' This is a healthy and immediately applicable idea. There are many things today deserving of that kick.

When I lived in Algiers, I would wait patiently all winter because I knew that in the course of one night, one cold, pure February night, the almond trees of the Vallée des Consuls would be covered with white flowers. I was then filled with delight as I saw this fragile snow stand up to all the rain and resist the wind from the sea. Yet every year it lasted, just long enough to prepare the fruit.

This is not a symbol. We shall not win our happiness with symbols. We shall need something more weighty. All I mean is that sometimes, when life weighs too heavily in this Europe still overflowing with its misery, I turn towards those shining lands where so much strength is still untouched. I know them too well not to realize that they are the chosen lands where courage and contemplation can live in harmony. The contemplation of their example then teaches me that if we would save the mind we must pass over its power to groan and exalt its strength and wonder. This world is poisoned by its misery, and seems to wallow in it. It has utterly surrendered to that evil which Nietzsche called the spirit of heaviness. Let us not contribute to it. It is vain to weep over the mind, it is enough to labour for it.

But where are the conquering virtues of the mind? This same Nietzsche listed them as the mortal enemies of the spirit of heaviness. For him they are strength of character, taste, the 'world', classical happiness, severe pride, the cold frugality of the wise. These virtues, more than ever, are necessary today, and each can choose the one that suits him best. Before the vastness of the undertaking, let no one in any case forget strength of character. I do not mean the one accompanied on electoral platforms by frowns and threats. But the one that, through the virtue of its whiteness and its sap, stands up to all the winds from the sea. It is that which, in the winter of the world, will prepare the fruit.

1940

Prometheus in the Underworld

I felt that the Gods lacked something so long as there was
nothing to set against them.

Prometheus in the Caucasus, Lucian

What is the meaning of Prometheus for the man of today?
It would doubtless be said that this God–defying rebel is
the model for contemporary man, and that his protest,
raised thousands of years ago in the deserts of Scythia, is
culminating today in an unparalleled historical convulsion.
But, at the same time, something tells us that this victim
of persecution is still among us, and that we are still deaf
to the great cry of human rebellion of which he gives the
solitary signal.

Modern man indeed endures a multitude of suffering
over the narrow surface of the earth, lacks foods and
warmth, and sees liberty as merely a luxury that can wait;
and all that he can do is suffer a little more, even as all
that liberty and its last witnesses can do is vanish a little
farther. Prometheus was the hero who loved men enough
to give them fire and liberty, technology and art. Today
mankind needs and cares only for technology. It rebels
through its machines, holding art and what art implies as
an obstacle and symbol of slavery. What, on the contrary,

characterizes Prometheus is that he cannot separate machines from art. He believes that both souls and bodies can be freed at the same time. The man of today believes that we must first of all free the body, even if the mind must suffer a provisional decease. But can the mind die provisionally? Indeed, if Prometheus were to come back to earth, the men of today would behave as the gods did long ago: they would nail him to the rock, in the name of that very humanism which he was the first to symbolize. The hostile voices that would then insult the defeated victim would be the very ones which echo on the threshold of Aeschylan tragedy: those of Force and Violence.

Am I yielding to the meanness of the times, to naked trees and the winter of the world? But this very nostalgia for light is my justification: it speaks to me of another world, of my true country. Does this nostalgia still mean something for some men? In the year the war began, I was to take ship and follow the voyage of Ulysses. At that time, even a penniless young man could form the sumptuous project of crossing the sea in quest of sunlight. But I then did as everyone else. I did not take ship. I took my place in the queue shuffling towards the open mouth of hell. Little by little, we entered. At the first cry of murdered innocence, the door slammed shut behind us. We were in hell, and we have not left it since. For six long years, we have been trying to come to terms with it. We now catch glimpses of the warm ghosts from the islands of the blessed only across the long, cold, sunless years which are still to come.

How then, in this damp, dark Europe, can we avoid trembling with regret and sharing this cry which in his old age Châteaubriand uttered to Ampère departing for Greece: 'You will rediscover neither a leaf of the olive-trees nor a pip of the grapes which I saw in Attica. I regret even the grass that grew there in my day. I have not had the strength to make a patch of heather grow.' And we too, sunk in spite of our youthful blood in the terrible old age of this last century, sometimes regret the grass which always grew, the olive leaf we shall no longer gaze on for itself, and the grapes of liberty. Man is everywhere, and everywhere we find his cries, his suffering and his threats. When so many men are gathered together, the grasshopper can find no space. History is a sterile earth where the heather will not grow. Yet the men of today have chosen history, and they neither could nor should have turned their faces from it. But instead of mastering it, they agree a little more each day to be its slave. It is here that they betray Prometheus, this son 'both bold in thought and light of heart'. It is here that they go back to the wretchedness of the men whom Prometheus tried to save. 'They saw without seeing, heard without listening, like figures in a dream.'

Yes, one evening in Provence, one whiff of salt is enough to show us that everything still lies before us. We need to reinvent fire, to reinstall those crafts which calm the body's hunger. Attica, the vine-harvest of liberty, the bread of the soul, must come later. What can we do but cry to ourselves: 'They will never more return, or they will return for others', and do what we must to see that others at least do not lack them? And what of us, who feel this painfully, and who yet try to accept it without bitterness? Are we lagging behind, or are we forging ahead? Shall we have the strength to make the heather grow again?

We can imagine how Prometheus would have replied to this question which arises in our country. Indeed, he has already given his answer: 'I promise you, O mortals, both improvement and repair, if you are skilful, virtuous and strong enough to achieve them with your own hands.' If, then, it is true that salvation lies in our own hands, I shall say Yes to the questions of this century, because of the wise strength and informed courage that I still feel in some of those I know. 'O Justice, O my mother,' cries Prometheus, 'you see what I am made to suffer.' And Hermes mocks the hero: 'I am amazed that, being half a god, you did not foresee the torment you now undergo.' 'I foresaw it,' replies the rebel. Those I have mentioned are, like him, the sons of justice. They too suffer from the misery of all men, knowing what they do. They indeed know that blind justice does not exist, that history has no eyes, and that we must therefore reject its justice in order to put in its place, in so far as this can be done, the justice invented by the mind. It is here that Prometheus comes once more back into our century.

Myths have no life of their own. They wait for us to clothe them in flesh. If one man in the world answers their call, they give us their strength in all its fullness. We must preserve this myth, and ensure that its sleep is not mortal so that resurrection may become possible. I sometimes doubt whether the men of today can be saved. But it is still possible to save their children, in both their body and their mind. It is possible to offer them at one and the same time the chances of happiness and those of beauty. If we must resign ourselves to living without beauty, and the liberty which it implies, the myth of Prometheus is one of those which remind us that any mutilation of man can only be temporary, and that we serve nothing in man if we do not serve the whole of man. If he is hungry for bread and for heather, and if it is true that bread is the more necessary, let us learn how to keep the memory of heather alive. At the darkest heart of history the men of Prometheus, without ceasing from their harsh calling, will keep watch over the earth and over the unwearying grass. The enchained hero maintains, amid the thunder and lightning of the Gods, his quiet faith in man. This is how he is harder than his rock and more patient than his vulture. More than his rebellion against the gods, it is this long stubbornness which is meaningful for us. It accompanies this admirable determination to separate and exclude nothing, and which always has and always will unite the suffering heart of men and the springtimes of the world.

1946

The gentleness of Algiers is rather Italian. The cruel glare of Oran is more like Spain. Perched high on a rock above the Rummel gorges, Constantine is reminiscent of Toledo. But Spain and Italy are overflowing with memories, with works of art and educative ruins. And Toledo has had its Greco and its Barrès. The cities I am discussing are, on the contrary, towns without a past. They are towns which offer neither relaxation nor tenderness. When the siesta hours bring their boredom, there is neither compassion nor melancholy in their sadness. In the morning light, or in the natural luxury of the evenings, their delights are, on the contrary, without gentleness. These towns give nothing to the mind and everything to the passions. They are suited neither to wisdom nor to the refinements of taste. A Barrès and those like him would be crushed to pieces.

Passionate travellers (of other people's passions), over-sensitive minds, aesthetes and newly-weds have nothing to gain from going to Algiers. And, unless he has an absolute vocation, no one could be recommended to retire and live there for ever. Sometimes, in Paris, when people I esteem ask me about Algiers, I feel like crying out: 'Don't go there.' Such a joke would have some truth in it. For I can see what they are expecting and know they will not obtain it. And, at the same time, I know the charms and the subtle power of this country, its insinuating hold on those who linger there, how it immobilizes them, first of all by ridding them of questions, and finally by rocking them to sleep in everyday life. When the light hits you, so glaring that it turns black and white, it almost stops you breathing. You give way to it, settle down in it, and then realize that this too long splendour holds nothing for the soul and is merely an excessive delight. You would then like to turn back to the mind. But the men of this country, and that is their strength, seem stronger in heart than mind. They can be your friends (and what friends!), but you can never tell them your secrets. Such a thing might be considered rather fearsome here in Paris, where souls are poured out so lavishly and where the water of secrets flows softly and endlessly along among the fountains, statues and the gardens.

What this land most resembles is Spain. But with no traditions, Spain would be merely a beautiful desert. And unless they happen to have been born there, there is only one race of men who can think of withdrawing for ever to the desert. Since I was born in this desert, I cannot in any case consider discussing it as a visitor. Can one number the charms of a dearly loved woman? No, you love her all of a piece, if I may use the expression, with one or two precise reasons for tenderness such as a favourite pout or a 43 particular way of shaking the head. I thus have a long-standing liaison with Algeria, one that will doubtless never end, and which prevents me from being completely lucid. All you can do in such a case is, by perseverance, to make a kind of abstract list of what you love in the thing you love. It is this academic exercise that I can undertake here in respect of Algeria.

First of all comes the beauty of its young people. The Arabs, of course, and then the others. The French of Algeria are a bastard race, made up of unforeseen mixtures. Spaniards and Alsatians, Italians, Maltese, Jews and Greeks have come together there. As in America this brutal interbreeding has had happy results. As you walk through Algiers, look at the wrists of the women and the young men, and then think of the ones you see in the Paris *métro*.

The traveller who is still young will also notice that the women there are beautiful. The best place to take full note of this is the terrace of the Café des Facultés, in the Rue Michelet, in Algiers, on a Sunday morning in April. Cohorts of young women, sandals on their feet, wearing light, brightly coloured dresses, walk up and down the street. You can admire them without inhibitions: that is why they are there. At Oran the Cintra bar on the Boulevard Gallieni is also a good observatory. At Constantine you can always walk round the bandstand. But since the sea is several hundred kilometres away, there is something lacking in the people you meet there. In general, and because of this geographical location, Constantine offers fewer attractions, though its boredom has a rather more delicate quality.

If the traveller arrives in summer, the first thing he must obviously do is go down on to the beaches which surround the towns. He will see the same young people, more dazzling because less clothed. The sun then gives them the somnolent eyes of great beasts. In this respect the beaches of Oran are the finest, for nature and women are both wilder there.

As far as picturesqueness is concerned, Algiers offers an Arab town, Oran a Negro village and a Spanish district, and Constantine a Jewish quarter. Algiers has a long necklace of boulevards along the sea; you must walk there at night. Oran has few trees, but the finest stones in the world. Constantine has a suspension bridge where the thing to do is have your photograph taken. On very windy days the bridge sways to and fro above the deep gorges of the Rummel, and you have a feeling of danger.

I recommend the sensitive traveller, if he goes to Algiers, to go and drink *anisette* under the archways around the port, to go in the morning to La Pêcherie and eat freshly caught fish grilled on charcoal stoves; to go and listen to Arab music in a little café in the Rue de la Lyre whose name I have forgotten; to sit on the ground at six in the evening at the foot of the statue of the Duc 45 d'Orléans in Government Square (not for the sake of the duke, but because there are people walking by, and it is pleasant there); to go and lunch at the Padovani restaurant, which is a kind of dance-hall on stilts, on the sea shore, where life is always easy; to visit the Arab cemeteries, first of all to find calm and beauty there, and then to appreciate at their true value the ignoble cities where we stack our dead; to go and smoke a cigarette in the Rue des Bouchers, in the Kasbah, in the midst of the spleens, livers, mesenteries and bleeding lungs that are dripping everywhere (the cigarette is necessary, since these middle ages have a strong smell).

For the rest, you must be able to speak ill of Algiers when in Oran (insisting on the commercial superiority of Oran as a port), make fun of Oran when in Algiers (have no hesitation in accepting the idea that the Oranais 'do not know how to live'), and, at every opportunity, humbly acknowledge the superiority of Algiers over metropolitan France. Once these concessions have been made, you will be able to appreciate the real superiority of the Algerian over the Frenchman, that is to say his limitless generosity and his natural hospitality.

It is perhaps here that I could stop all irony. After all, the best way of talking about what you love is to speak of it lightly. As far as Algeria is concerned, I am always afraid to lean on this matching inner chord, whose blind and serious song I know so well. But I can at least say that it is my true country, and that anywhere in the world I recognize its sons and my brothers by the friendly laughter that seizes me when I meet them. Yes, what I love about the towns of Algiers does not cut me off from the men who live in them. That is why I prefer to be there at that evening hour when the shops and offices pour out into the streets, still dark from the sun, a chattering crowd which flows right along to the boulevards facing the sea. There, it begins to grow silent as the night falls, and as the lights from the sky, from the lighthouses in the bay and from the streetlamps, merge gradually into the same quivering glow. A whole people then stands meditating on the sea shore, and the crowd splits up into a thousand solitudes. Then begin the great African nights, royal exile, and the exaltation of despair which awaits the solitary traveller.

No, you must certainly not go there if you feel a lukewarm heart and if your soul is weak and weary! But for those who know what it is like to be torn between yes and no, between noon and midnight, between revolt and love, and finally for those who love funeral-pyres along the shore, there is a flame awaiting them in Algiers.

1947

Helen's Exile

The Mediterranean has its sunlit tragedy which is not that of the mists. On certain evenings, on the sea, at the foot of the mountains, night falls on the perfect curve of a little bay, and an anguished fullness rises from the silent waters. We realize in such places that, if the Greeks experienced despair, it was always through beauty and its oppressive quality. Tragedy, in this golden sadness, reaches its highest point. Our own time, on the contrary, has nourished its despair in ugliness and in convulsions. That is why Europe would be ignoble if grief could ever have this quality.

We have exiled beauty, the Greeks took up arms on its behalf. A first but a long-standing difference. Greek thought always took its stand upon the idea of limit. It carried nothing to extremes, neither religion nor reason, because it denied nothing, neither reason nor religion. It gave everything its share, balancing light with shade. Our Europe, on the contrary, eager for the conquest of totality, is the daughter of excess. It denies beauty, as it denies everything which it does not extol. And, although in diverse ways, it extols only one thing: the future empire of reason. In its madness it pushes back the eternal limits, and at once dark Furies swoop down upon it to destroy.

Nemesis is watching, goddess of moderation, not of vengeance. All those who go beyond the limit are by her pitilessly chastised.

The Greeks, who spent centuries asking themselves what was just, would understand nothing of our idea of justice. Equity, for them, supposed a limit, while our whole continent is convulsed by the quest for a justice which it sees as absolute. At the dawn of Greek thought Heraclitus already conceived justice as setting its bounds to the physical universe itself. 'The sun will not go beyond its bounds, for otherwise the Furies which watch over justice will find it out.' We, who have cast both the universe and the mind from their proper orbit, laugh at such threats. We light up in a drunken sky what suns we please. But these bounds nevertheless exist and we know it. In our wildest madness we dream of a balance that we have lost, and which in our simplicity we think we shall rediscover when our errors cease. An infantile presumption, and one which justifies the fact that childish peoples, inheriting our madness, should guide our history today.

A fragment attributed to this same Heraclitus states simply: 'Presumption, regression of progress.' And, many centuries after the Ephesian, Socrates, threatened by the death penalty, granted himself no other superiority than this: that he did not presume to know what he did not. The most exemplary life and ideas which these centuries can offer end on a proud acknowledgement of ignorance. 49

And, in forgetting this, we have forgotten our virility. We have preferred the power which apes greatness, Alexander first of all, and then the Roman conquerors, which our school history books, by an incomparable vulgarity of soul, teach us to admire. We have conquered in our turn, have set aside the bounds, mastered heaven and earth. Our reason has swept everything away. Alone at last, we finally hold empire over a desert. How could we conceive this higher balance in which nature balanced history, beauty and goodness, and which carried the music of poetry even into the tragedy of blood? We turn our back upon nature, we are ashamed of beauty. Our miserable tragedies stink of offices, and the blood they run with has the colour of dirty ink.

That is why it is indecent to proclaim today that we are the sons of Greece. Or, if we are, we are sons turned renegade. Putting history on the throne of God, we are marching towards theocracy, like those whom the Greeks called barbarians and whom they fought to the last in the waters of Salamis. If we really want to grasp our difference, we must address ourselves to the man who, among our philosophers, is the true rival of Plato. 'Only the modern town', Hegel dares write, 'can offer the mind the ground where it can achieve awareness of itself.' Thus we live in the time of great cities. The world has been deliberately cut off from what gave it permanence: nature, the sea, hills, evening meditations. Awareness can now be found only in the streets, because there is history only in the streets, so runs the decree. And, consequently, our most significant works bear witness to the same prejudice. One seeks in vain for landscapes in major European writers since Dostoyevsky. History explains neither the natural universe which came before it, nor beauty, which stands above it. It has consequently chosen to know nothing of them. Whereas Plato contained everything, nonsense, reason and myths, our philosophers contain nothing except either nonsense or reason, because they have closed their eyes to the rest. The mole is meditating.

It was Christianity that began to replace the contemplation of the world by the tragedy of the soul. But Christianity at least referred to a spiritual nature, and consequently maintained a certain fixity. Now that God is dead, all that remains is history and power. For a long time now, the whole effort of our philosophers has been aimed solely at replacing the idea of human nature by the idea of situation, and ancient harmony by the confused upsurge of chance, or by the pitiless movement of reason. While the Greeks used reason to restrain the will, we have ended by placing the upsurge of the will at the heart of reason, and reason has therefore become murderous. For the Greeks, values were pre-existent to every action, and marked out its exact limits. Modern philosophy places its values at the end of action. They are not, but they become; and we shall know them completely only at the end of history. When they disappear, limits do as well, and since ideas differ on what these will be, since there is no struggle which, unhindered by these same values, does not extend indefinitely, we are now witnessing a conflict of Messianisms whose clamours merge in the shock of empires. Excess is a fire, according to Heraclitus. The fire is gaining ground; Nietzsche has been overtaken. It is no longer with hammer blows but with cannon shots that Europe philosophizes.

Nature is still there, nevertheless. It sets up its calm skies and its reasons against the folly of men. Until the atom too bursts into flame, and history ends in the triumph of reason and the death agony of the species. But the Greeks never said that the limit could not be crossed. They said that it existed and that the man who dared ignore it was mercilessly struck down. There is nothing in the history of today that can contradict them.

Both the historical spirit and the artist seek to remake the world. But the artist, through an obligation of his very nature, recognizes the limits which the historical mind ignores. This is why the latter aims at tyranny while the passion of the first is liberty. All those who are fighting today for liberty are in the final analysis fighting for beauty. Of course, no one thinks of defending beauty solely for its own sake. Beauty cannot do without man, and we shall give our time its greatness and serenity only by accompanying it into its misery. We shall never again stand alone. But it is equally true that man cannot do without beauty, and this is what our time pretends to forget. It tenses itself to achieve empires and the absolute, it seeks to transfigure the world before having exhausted it, to set it to rights before having understood it. Whatever it may say, it is turning its back on this world. Ulysses, on Calypso's island, is given the choice between immortality and the land of his fathers. He chooses this earth, and death with it. Such a simple greatness is today foreign to our minds. Others will say that we lack humility. But this word, all things considered, is ambiguous. Like those buffoons in Dostoyevsky who boast of everything, rise up to the stars and end by flaunting their shame in the first public place, we lack simply the pride of the man who is faithful to his limitations and perceptively in love with his condition.

'I hate my time,' said Saint-Exupery before his death, for reasons that are not far removed from those which I have mentioned. But, however overwhelming this cry may be, coming from him who loved men for their admirable qualities, we shall not take it as our own. Yet what a temptation, at certain times, to turn our back upon this gaunt and gloomy world. But this is our time and we cannot live hating ourselves. It has fallen so low as much by the excess of its virtues as by the greatness of its faults. We shall fight for the one amongst its virtues that comes from far off. Which virtue? Patroclus's horses weep for their master, dead in battle. All is lost. But Achilles returns to the fray and victory lies at the end because friendship has been murdered: friendship is a virtue.

It is by acknowledging our ignorance, refusing to be fanatics, recognizing the boundaries of man and the world, through the faces we love, in short, through beauty, that we shall rejoin the Greeks. In a way, the meaning of tomorrow's history will not be where men think it is. It lies in the struggle between creation and the inquisition. Whatever the price that artists will have to pay for their empty hands, we can hope for their victory. Once again, the philosophy of darkness will melt away above the dazzling sea. Oh, noonday thought, the Trojan war is fought far from the battle ground! Once again, the terrible walls of the modern city will fall to deliver, 'its soul serene as the untroubled waves', Helen's beauty.

1948

The Enigma

Waves of sunlight, pouring from the topmost sky, bounce fiercely on the countryside around us. All falls quiet with this din, and Mount Luberon, over there, is merely a vast block of silence which I listen to unceasingly. I listen carefully, someone runs to me from far off, invisible friends call to me, my joy grows, the same joy as years ago. Once again, a happy enigma helps me to understand everything.

Where is the absurdity of the world? In this shining glory, or in the memory of its absence? How, with so much sun in my memory, could I have wagered on nonsense? People around me are amazed; so, at times, am I. I could tell them, as I tell myself, that it was in fact the sun which helped me, and that the very thickness of its light coagulates the universe and its forms into a dazzling blackness. But there are other ways of saying this, and I should like, faced by this white and black clarity which for me has always been that of truth, to explain in simple terms what I feel about this absurdity which I know too well to allow anyone to speak about it in an oversimplified way. Moreover, the very fact of talking about it will lead us back to the sun.

No man can say what he is. But he can sometimes say what he is not. People want the man who is still seeking to have already reached his conclusions. A thousand voices are already telling him what he has found, and yet he knows that this is not the case. Should he carry on seeking and let them talk? Of course. But, from time to time, we must defend ourselves. I do not know what I am looking for, I name it prudently. I withdraw what I said, I repeat myself. I go backwards and forwards. People nevertheless call upon me to deliver the name, or names, once and for all. Then I object; are not things lost when they receive a name? Here, at least, is what I can try to say.

If I am to believe one of my friends, a man always has two characters: his own, and the one his wife thinks he has. If we replace his wife by society, we shall understand how a particular expression, used by a writer to describe a whole context of emotions, can be isolated by the way people comment on it and presented to its author every time he tries to talk about something else. Words are like actions: 'Are you the father of this child?' 'Yes.' 'Then he is your son.' 'It is not as simple as that, not at all!' Thus Gérard de Nerval, one filthy night, hanged himself twice, once for himself because he was unhappy, and a second time for his legend, which now helps some people to live. No one can write about real unhappiness, or about certain moments of happiness, and I shall not try to do so here. But, as far as legends are concerned, we can describe them, and, for a moment at least, believe that we have dispelled them.

A writer writes to a great extent to be read (as for those who say they don't, let us admire them but not believe them). Yet more and more, in France, he writes in order to obtain that final consecration which lies in not being read. From the moment, in fact, that he can provide the material for a picturesque article in one of our mass-circulation newspapers, there is every possibility that he will be known to a fairly large number of people who will never read his works because they will be content to know his name and to read what other people write about him. From then onwards, he will be known (and forgotten) not for what he is, but according to the image which a hurried journalist has given of him. To make a name in literature, it is consequently no longer indispensable to write books. It is enough to be thought to have written one book, mentioned in the evening papers, and on which one can repose for the rest of one's life.

There is no doubt that this reputation, great or small, will be undeserved. But what can be done about it? Let us rather admit that this inconvenience can be beneficial. Doctors know that certain illnesses are desirable: they provide, in their own way, a compensation for a functional disorder which, in their absence, would express itself in a more serious disturbance. Thus there are fortunate 57 constipations and providential attacks of arthritis. The flood of words and hasty judgements, which nowadays drowns all public activity in an ocean of frivolity, at least endows the French writer with a modesty that he constantly needs in a nation which, moreover, gives a disproportionate importance to his calling. To see your name in two or three newspapers I could mention is so harsh a trial that it must inevitably involve some spiritual benefit. Let us then praise society, which can so cheaply teach us every day, by its very homages, that the greatness which it honours is worthless. The louder the sound, the quicker it dies. It evokes that fire of tow which Alexander VI often had burned before him to remind him that all the glory of this world vanishes like smoke.

But that is enough irony. It is enough, in this respect, to say that an artist should cheerfully resign himself to allowing what he knows is an unworthy image of himself to lie about in dentists' and hairdressers' waiting-rooms. It was there that I read about a fashionable author who was considered to spend every night presiding over heady Bacchanalian orgies, where nymphs were clothed in nothing but their hair and fauns had dark and fatal nails. One might doubtless have wondered how he found the time to write a series of books that filled several library shelves. This writer, in fact, like many of his colleagues, sleeps at night in order to spend long hours every day working at

his desk, and drinks Vichy water so as not to strain his

liver. This does not prevent the average Frenchman, whose Saharan sobriety and mania for cleanliness are well known, from being indignant at the idea that our writers should teach men to drink and not to wash. There is no lack of examples. I can myself give an excellent recipe of how to secure a reputation for austerity very cheaply. I do in fact bear the weight of such a reputation, which is a source of great amusement to my friends (as far as I myself am concerned, it is more a source of embarrassment, for I know how little I deserve it). All you need do, for example, is decline the honour of dining with a newspaper editor of whom you do not have a high opinion. Even simple decency cannot be imagined except by reference to some twisted sickness of the soul. In any case, no one will ever imagine that, if you refuse this editor's dinner, this is not only because you do not have a very high opinion of him, but also because your greatest fear in the world is being bored – and what is more boring than a typically Parisian dinner?

We must therefore be resigned. But from time to time you can try to readjust the sights, and to repeat that you cannot always be a painter of the absurd and that no one can believe in a literature of despair. Of course, it is always possible to write, or to have written, an essay on the notion of the absurd. But, after all, you can also write about incest without having necessarily hurled yourself on your unfortunate sister; and I have nowhere read that

Sophocles ever thought of killing his father and dishonouring his mother. The idea that every writer necessarily writes about himself and depicts himself in his books is one of the puerile notions that we have inherited from Romanticism. It is by no means impossible, on the contrary, that a writer should be interested first and foremost in other people, or in his time, or in familiar myths. Even if he does happen to put himself in the picture, it is only very exceptionally that he talks about what he is really like. A man's works often retrace the story of his nostalgias or his temptations, practically never his own story, especially when they claim to be autobiographical. No man has ever dared describe himself as he is.

As far as such a thing is possible, I would, on the contrary, have liked to be an objective writer. What I call an objective writer is an author who chooses themes without ever taking himself as the subject. But the modern mania of identifying the author with his subject-matter cannot allow him to enjoy this relative liberty. Thus one becomes a prophet of the absurd. Yet what did I do except reason about an idea which I found in the streets of my time? It goes without saying that both I and my whole generation have nourished this idea (and that a part of myself still does so). What I did, however, was to set it far enough from me to analyse it and decide on its logic. Everything that I have been able to write since then is sufficient proof of this. But it is more convenient to exploit a cliché than a nuance. They choose the cliché: so I am absurd as before.

What is the point of saying yet again that in the experience which interested me, and on which I happened to write, the absurd can be considered only as a point of departure – even though the memory and feeling of it still accompany the later steps in the argument? Similarly, with all due sense of proportion, Cartesian doubt, which is systematic, is not enough to make Descartes into a sceptic. In any case, how could one restrict oneself to saying that everything is meaningless, and that we should plunge into absolute despair? Without going to the root of the matter, one can at least remark that in the same way as there is no absolute materialism, since simply to form this word there must be something in the world apart from matter, there is likewise no total nihilism. As soon as you say that everything is nonsense, you express something that is meaningful. Refusing to see the world all meaning amounts to abolishing all value judgements. But living and eating, for example, is in itself a value judgement. You choose to stay alive the moment you do not allow yourself to die of hunger, and you consequently recognize that life has at least a relative value. What, in fact, does a literature of despair mean? Despair is silent. Moreover, even silence is meaningful if your eyes speak. True despair is the agony of death, the grave or the abyss. If it speaks, if it reasons, above all if it writes, immediately a brother reaches out his hand, the tree is justified, love is born. A literature of despair is a contradiction in terms.

Of course, a certain optimism is not my speciality. Like all the men of my age, I grew up to the sound of the drums of the First World War, and our history since that time has remained murder, injustice or violence. But real pessimism, which does exist, lies in adding something to all this cruelty and shame. For my part, I have never ceased fighting against this dishonour, and I hate only the cruel. In our darkest nihilism I have sought only reasons to go beyond it. Not, I would add, through virtue, nor by a rare elevation of the soul, but by an instinctive fidelity to a light in which I was born, and in which for thousands of years men have learned to welcome life even in suffering. Aeschylus is often full of despair; yet he sheds light and warmth. At the centre of his universe, we find not flesh-less nonsense but an enigma, that is to say a meaning which is difficult to decipher because it dazzles us. And, likewise, the unworthy but nevertheless stubborn sons of Greece who still survive in this emaciated century may still find this history too scalding hot, and yet they bear the pain because they want to understand it. At the centre of our work, dark though it may be, there shines an inexhaustible sun, the same sun which cries today across the hills and plain.

62 After this, the fire of tow can burn; what do our image

and our usurpations matter? What we are, what we have to be, are enough to fill our lives and occupy our strength. Paris is a marvellous cave, and its men, seeing their own shadows reflected on the far wall, take them for the only reality there is. The same is true of the strange and fleeting fame this town awards. But we have learned, far from Paris, that there is a light behind us, and that we must turn round and cast off our chains if we are to look at it directly; that our task is, before we die, to seek for all the words we can to name it. Each artist is undoubtedly pursuing his truth. If he is a great artist, each work brings him nearer to it, or, at least, itself swings closer in towards this centre, this buried sun where everything must one day burn. If he is mediocre, each work takes him farther from it, the centre is then everywhere, the light disintegrates. But the only people who can help the artist in his obstinate quest are those who love him, and those who, themselves lovers or creators, find in their own passion the measure for all passion, and can then judge.

Yes, all this noise . . . when peace would be to love and create in silence! But we must learn to be patient. One moment more, the sun seals our mouths.

1950

Return to Tipasa

> You have sailed with a furious soul far from your father's
> house, beyond the double rocks of the sea, and you live
> in a foreign land.
>
> *Medea*

For five days, the rain had been falling unceasingly on
Algiers, and had finally drenched the sea itself. From the
heights of an apparently inexhaustible sky, unending sheets
of rain, so thick they were viscous, swooped down on the
gulf. Soft and grey like a great sponge, the sea heaved in
the shapeless bay. But the surface of the water seemed
almost motionless beneath the steady rain. At long intervals, however, a broad and imperceptible movement raised
a murky cloud of steam from off the sea and brought it
into harbour, beneath a circle of soaking boulevards. The
town itself, all its white walls running with damp, gave off
another cloud of steam which moved out to meet the first.
Wherever you turned when this happened, you seemed to
be breathing water, and you could drink the very air.

Looking at this drowned sea, I walked about and waited,
in this December Algiers which was still for me the town
of summers. I had fled from the night of Europe, from a
winter of faces. But the town of summers had itself been

emptied of its laughter and offered me only hunched and shining backs. In the evening, in the violently lit cafés where I sought refuge, I read my age upon faces that I could recognize without giving them a name. All I knew was that these men had been young when I was, and that now they were young no more.

I stayed on, however, without any clear idea of what I was waiting for, except, perhaps, the moment when I could go back to Tipasa. It is, indeed, a great folly and one that is almost always punished, to go back to the places of your youth, and to seek to relive, at the age of forty, things which you loved or greatly enjoyed at twenty. But I knew about this folly. I had already come back to Tipasa for a first time, shortly after those wartime years that marked for me the end of my youth. I then hoped, I believe, to rediscover a liberty which I could not forget. Here, indeed, more than twenty years ago, I had spent whole mornings wandering among the ruins, breathing the scent of absinthe, warming myself against the stones, finding the small roses which survive in springtime and swiftly lose their leaves. Only at noon, when the very crickets fell silent in the heat, would I flee before the avid blaze of an all-devouring light. Sometimes at night I would sleep open-eyed beneath a sky flowing with stars. Then I was alive. Fifteen years afterwards I found my ruins again, a few steps from the first waves. I followed the streets of the forgotten city across the fields covered with bitter trees, and, on the hills overlooking the bay, could still caress the breadcrust-coloured pillars. But now the ruins were surrounded by barbed wire, and could be reached only through official entrances. It was also forbidden, for reasons which apparently enjoyed the blessing of morality, to walk there after dark; by day you met a sworn guardian. And that morning, doubtless by chance, it was raining over the whole area of the ruins.

Bewildered, walking through the lonely and rain-soaked countryside, I at least made an effort to rediscover that strength which has so far never failed me, and which helps me to accept what exists once I have recognized that I cannot change it. And could not, in fact, travel backwards through time, restore to the world the face that I had loved and which had disappeared in the course of one day, many years ago. On the second of September, in fact, I had not gone to Greece, as I had planned. Instead, war had come to us, then had covered Greece itself. This distance, these years which separated the warm ruins from the barbed wire were also in myself, as I stood that day before the sarcophagi filled with black water or under the dripping tamarisk trees. Brought up first of all in the spectacle of beauty, which was my only wealth, I had begun with fullness. What had followed was barbed wire: I mean tyrannies, war, police forces, the time of revolt. We had had to come to terms with the night: the beauty of the day was only a memory. And in this muddy Tipasa, the memory itself was growing dim. No talk now of beauty, fullness or youth! In the light cast by the flames, the world had suddenly shown its wrinkles and its wounds, both old and new. It had grown old in an instant, the twinkling of an eye, and we with it. I knew well enough that only men caught unawares could be inspired by the passion which I sought for here. Love cannot exist without a little innocence. Where was innocence? Empires were crumbling, men and nations tearing at one another's throats; our mouths were sullied. After being innocent in ignorance, we were now unintentionally guilty: the more we knew, the greater grew the mystery. This is why we busied ourselves, Oh! mockery of mockeries, with morality. Sick in spirit, I dreamed of virtue! In the days of innocence, I did not know that morality existed. I now knew that it did, and could not live up to it. On the promontory that I had loved in former days, between the drenched pillars of the ruined temple, I seemed to be walking behind someone whose footsteps I could still hear on the tombstones and mosaics, but whom I should never catch up with again. I went back to Paris, where I stayed for some years before coming back home.

During all these years, however, I had an obscure feeling that something was lacking. When you have once had the chance to love intensely, your life is spent seeking to find this light and ardour once again. To give up beauty and the sensual happiness it brings and devote myself exclusively to unhappiness requires a greatness that I do not have. But, after all, nothing is true which compels us to exclude. Isolated beauty ends in grimaces, solitary justice in oppression. Anyone who seeks to serve the one to the exclusion of the other serves nobody, not even himself, and in the end is doubly the servant of injustice. A day comes when, because we have held ourselves so stiff, nothing amazes us any more, and our life is spent in beginning again. These are days of exile, dryness and dead souls. To live again, we need grace, forgetfulness of ourselves, or else a homeland. On some mornings, as we turn a corner, an exquisite dew falls on our heart and then vanishes. But its freshness still remains, and it is always this which the heart demands. I had to leave once more.

And, in Algiers for a second time, still walking under the same downpour which I felt had not stopped since a departure which I had considered final, in the midst of this immense melancholy which smelled of rain and sea, in spite of this misty sky, these backs fleeing beneath the deluge, these cafés whose sulphurous light decomposed people's faces, I still persisted in my hopes. Did I not know, moreover, that rain in Algiers, although looking as if it is going on for ever, nevertheless does stop quite suddenly, like those rivers in my country which swell to a flood in two hours, devastate acres of land, and dry up again in an instant? One evening, in fact, the rain stopped.

I waited for yet another night. A liquid morning rose, dazzling, over the pure sea. From the sky, fresh as a rose, washed and rewashed by the waters, reduced by each successive laundering to its most delicate and clearest texture, there fell a quivering light which gave each house, each tree, a palpable shape and a magic newness. The earth, on the morning the world was born, must have arisen in just such a light. Once again I set out for Tipasa.

There is not a single one of these sixty-nine kilometres that is not filled for me with memories and sensations. A violent childhood, adolescent day-dreams to the hum of the bus's engines, mornings, the freshness of young girls, beaches, young muscles always tensed to their highest effort, that slight anguish which evening brings to a heart of sixteen years, desire for life, glory, and always the same sky as companion to all the years, with its inexhaustible strength and light, a sky insatiable and continually devouring, for months on end, the victims lying crucified upon the beach at the funereal hour of noon. Always the same sea as well, almost impalpable in the morning air, which I glimpsed again on the horizon as soon as the road left the Sahel and the bronze-coloured vineyards on its hills, and plunged down towards the coast. But I did not stop to look at it. I wanted to see the Chenoua again, this heavy, solid mountain, carved in one piece and running along the west side of Tipasa Bay before plunging into the sea. You see it from far off, long before you arrive, as a light blue haze still mingling with the sea. But it gradually condenses as you come nearer, until it takes on the colour of the waters which surround it, like an immense and motionless wave brutally caught in the very act of breaking over a suddenly calm sea. Nearer still, almost at the gates of Tipasa, you see its beetling mass, brown and green, the old, unshakeable, mossgrown god, port and haven for its sons, of whom I am one.

I was gazing at it as I finally crossed the barbed wire and stood among the ruins. And, in the glorious December light, as happens only once or twice in lives that can henceforth see themselves as crowned with every blessing, I found exactly what I had come to seek, and which, in spite of time and in spite of the world, was given truly to myself alone in this deserted nature. From the olive-strewn forum you could see the village opposite. Not a sound came from it: wisps of smoke rose in the limpid air. The sea also lay silent, as if breathless beneath the unending shower of cold and glittering light. From the Chenoua a distant cock-crow alone extolled the fragile glory of the day. Across the ruins, as far as the eye could see, there lay nothing but pock-marked stones and absinthe plants, trees and perfect columns in the transparence of the crystal air. It was as if the morning stood still, as if the sun had stopped for an immeasurable moment. Amid this light and silence, years of night and fury melted slowly away. I
listened to an almost forgotten sound within myself, as if

my heart had long been stopped and was now gently beginning to beat again. And, now awake, I recognized one by one the imperceptible sounds that made up the silence: the continuous bass part of the birds, the short, light sighing of the sea at the foot of the rocks, the vibration of the trees, the blind song of the columns, the whispering of the absinthe plants, the furtive lizards. I could hear all that, while also listening to the waves of happiness rising up within me. I felt that I had at last come back to port, for a moment at least, and that from henceforth this moment would never end. But shortly afterwards the sun visibly rose a degree higher in the sky. A blackbird chirped its brief prelude and immediately, from all around, birds' voices exploded with a strength, a jubilation, a joyful discord, an infinite delight. The day moved on. It was to carry me through till evening.

At noon, on the half-sandy slopes, strewn with heliotropes as if by a foam which the furious waves of the last few days had left behind them in their retreat, I gazed at the sea, then gently rising and falling as if exhausted, and quenched the two thirsts that cannot long be neglected if all our being is not to dry up, the thirst to love and the thirst to admire. For there is only misfortune in not being loved; there is misery in not loving. We all, today, are dying of this misery. This is because blood and hatred lay bare the heart itself: the long demand for justice exhausts the love which nevertheless gave it birth. In the clamour 71 in which we live love is impossible and justice not enough. This is why Europe hates the daylight and can do nothing but confront one injustice with another. But I rediscovered at Tipasa that, in order to prevent justice from shrivelling up, from becoming a magnificent orange containing only a dry and bitter pulp, we had to keep a freshness and a source of joy intact within ourselves, loving the daylight which injustice leaves unscathed, and returning to the fray with this reconquered light. Here once more I found ancient beauty, a young sky, and measured my good fortune as I realized at last that in the worst years of our madness the memory of this sky had never left me. It was this which in the end had saved me from despair. I had always known that the ruins of Tipasa were younger than our new buildings or our crumbling towns. There, the world was born again each morning in a light that was always new. O light! This is the cry of all the characters who, in classical tragedy, come face to face with their destiny. Their final refuge was also ours, and I now knew that this was so. In the depths of the winter I finally learned that there lay in me an unconquerable summer.

Once again I left Tipasa, returning to Europe and its struggles. But the memory of this day still bears me up and helps me greet with equanimity both joys and woes. What can I long for, at the difficult moment where now we stand, except the power to exclude nothing and learn to weave from strands of black and white one single rope that is stretched to breaking point? In everything which I have done or said up to now, I seem to recognize these two forces, even when they contradict each other. I have not been able to deny the light where I was born, and I have not wished to reject the servitudes of our time. It would be too easy to place here by the side of Tipasa other names which are more sonorous and more cruel: for the men of today there is an inner path which I know well through having travelled both ways upon it, and which leads from the hills of the mind to the capitals of crime. And, doubtless, we can always take rest, sleep on the hillside or settle down in crime. But if we give up a part of what exists, we must ourselves give up being; we must then give up living or loving except by proxy. Thus there is a will to live while refusing nothing of what life offers which is the virtue that I honour most in all this world. From time to time, at least, it is true that I should like to have exercised it. Since few epochs more than our own require us to be equal to the best as to the worst, I should like, in fact, to elude nothing and keep a double memory alive. Yes, there is beauty and there are the humiliated. Whatever difficulties the enterprise may present, I should like never to be unfaithful either to the second or the first.

But this still sounds like ethics, and we live for something that goes beyond them. If we could name it, what silence would ensue! On the hill of Sainte-Salsa, to the east of Tipasa, the evening is inhabited. Darkness, it is true, has not yet come, but an invisible waning of the light foreshadows sunset. A wind rises, gentle as the night, and suddenly the untroubled sea chooses its way and flows like a great barren river across the horizon. The sky grows darker. What follows is mystery, the gods of night, and what lies on the other side of pleasure. But how can this be expressed? The small coin that I take away from here has one clear side, the face of a beautiful woman which constantly repeats all I have learned today, and a side which is eaten away and which I feel under my fingers during my return. What can this lipless mouth do except repeat what another, mysterious voice within me says, a voice which daily teaches me my ignorance and happiness:

'The secret that I am looking for is buried in a valley of olive trees under the grass and cold violets, around an old house that smells of vines. For more than twenty years I have wandered over this valley, and over others like it, questioning dumb goat-herds, knocking at the door of uninhabited ruins. Sometimes, when the first star shines in a still clear sky, beneath a rain of delicate light, I have thought that I knew. I did know, in fact. Perhaps I still know. But no one wants this secret, doubtless I myself do not desire it, and cannot cut myself off from my own people. I live with my family, which believes that it reigns over rich and hideous towns, built of stones and fogs. Day and night it raises its voice, and everything yields while it bows down before nothing: it is deaf to all secrets. Its power, which bears me up, nevertheless bores me, and I come to be weary of its cries. But its unhappiness is my own, we are of the same blood. I too am sick, and am I not a noisy accomplice who has cried out among the stones? Thus I try to forget, I march through our towns of iron and fire, I smile bravely at the night, I welcome storms, I shall be faithful. In fact, I have forgotten: henceforth, I shall be deaf and active. But perhaps one day, when we are ready to die of ignorance and exhaustion, I shall be able to give up our gaudy tombs, go and lie down in the valley, under the unchanging light, and learn for a last time what I know.'

1953

The Sea Close By

LOGBOOK

I grew up in the sea and poverty was sumptuous, then I lost the sea and found all luxuries grey and poverty unbearable. Since then, I have been waiting. I wait for the homebound ships, the house of the waters, the limpidity of day. I wait patiently, am polite with all my strength. Men see me walk by in fine and learned streets, I admire landscapes, applaud like everyone else, shake hands, but it is not me speaking. Men praise me, I dream a little, they insult me, I scarcely show surprise. Then I forget, and smile at the man who insulted me, or am too courteous in greeting the person I love. What can I do if all I can remember is one image? Finally they call upon me to tell them who I am. 'Nothing yet, nothing yet . . .'

It is at funerals that I excel myself. I do, indeed. I walk slowly through the iron-strewn paths of suburbs, travelling along wide lanes planted with cement trees and leading to holes in the cold earth. There, beneath the scarcely reddening bandage of the sky, I watch bold workmen inter my friends beneath six feet of earth. If I then cast the flower which a clay-covered hand holds out to me, it never misses the grave. My piety is exact, my feelings as they should be, my head is suitably inclined. I am admired for finding just the right word. But I have no merit in this: I am waiting.

I have been waiting for a long time. Sometimes, I stumble, I lose my touch, success evades me. What does it matter, for I am then alone. It is thus that I wake up at night, and, still half-asleep, think I hear the sound of waves and the breathing of the waters. Fully awake, I recognize the wind in the trees and the sad murmur of the empty town. I then need all my art to hide my distress or clothe it in the prevailing fashion.

At other times, on the contrary, I am helped. On certain days in New York, lost at the bottom of those wells of stones and steel where wander millions of men, I would run from one to another, without seeing where they ended, exhausted, until I was sustained only by the human mass seeking its way out. But, each time, the distant siren of a tug-boat came to remind me that this town, this empty well, was an island, and at the tip of the Battery the water of my baptism was awaiting me, black and rotting, covered over with hollow corks.

Thus, though I possess nothing, have given away my fortune, camp by the side of all my houses, I can still be blessed with all riches when I choose, set sail at every hour, unknown to despair. There is no country for those who despair, but I know that the sea comes before and after me, and hold my madness ready. Those who love and are separated can live in grief, but this is not despair: they know that love exists. This is why I suffer, dry-eyed, in exile. I am still waiting. A day comes, at last . . .

The bare feet of the sailors beat softly on the deck. It is 77 dawn, and we are setting sail. The moment we leave harbour, a short, gusty wind vigorously brushes the sea which curls backwards in small, foamless waves. A little later the wind freshens and scatters the sea with swiftly vanished camellias. Thus throughout the morning we hear our sails slapping over a cheerful pond. The waters are heavy, scaly, covered with cool foam. From time to time the waves yap against the bow; a bitter, unctuous foam, the God's saliva, flows along the wood and loses itself in the water where it scatters into shapes that die and are reborn, the hide of a white and blue cow, an exhausted beast which drifts a long way behind our wake.

Since our departure the seagulls have been following our ship, apparently without effort, almost without moving their wings. Their fine straight navigation scarcely leans upon the breeze. Suddenly, a loud plop at the level of the kitchens casts a greedy alarm among the birds, throws their fine flight into confusion and sends up a fire of white wings. The seagulls whirl madly in every direction, and then without any loss of speed drop away from the fight one by one and dive down to the sea. A few seconds later they are together again on the water, a quarrelsome farmyard that we leave behind us, nestling in the hollow of the wave, and slowly plucking through the manna of scraps.

78 At noon, under a deafening sun the sea, exhausted, scarcely

finds the strength to rise. When it falls back on itself, it makes the silence whistle. It cooks for an hour and the pale water, a vast white-hot iron sheet, sizzles. In a minute it will turn and offer its damp side, now hidden in waves and darkness, to the sun.

We pass by the gates of Hercules, the headland where Antaeus died. Beyond, the Ocean lies everywhere, on one side we pass by the Horn and the Cape of Good Hope, the Meridians wed the Latitudes, the Pacific drinks the Atlantic. Once our course is set for Vancouver, we plunge slowly towards the South Seas. A few cables' lengths away Easter Island, Desolation and the New Hebrides file past us in convoy. Suddenly one morning the seagulls disappear. We are far from any land, and alone, with our sails and our engines.

Alone also with the horizon. The waves come from the invisible East, patiently, one by one; they reach us, and then, patiently, set off again for the unknown West, one by one. A long voyage, with no beginning and no end . . . Rivers and streams pass by, the sea passes and remains. This is how we must love it, faithful and fleeting. I wed the sea.

The high seas. The sun sinks down, is swallowed by the mists long before it reaches the horizon. For one brief moment, the sea is pink on one side and blue on the other. Then the waters grow darker. The schooner slides, minute, over the surface of a perfect circle of thick, tarnished metal. And at the most peaceful hour, as evening comes, hundreds of porpoises emerge from the water, play around us for a moment, then flee to the horizon where there are no men. They leave behind them the silence and anguish of primitive waters.

A little later still, we meet an iceberg on the Tropic. Doubtless invisible after its long voyage in these warm waters, but still effective: it passes to starboard, where the rigging is briefly covered with a frosty dew, while to port the day dies without moisture.

Night does not fall at sea. Rather, from the depths of the waters, which an already submerged sun gradually darkens with its thick ashes, it rises towards the still pale sky. For a brief moment Venus shines alone above the black waves. In the twinkling of an eye, stars swarm in the liquid night.

The moon has risen. First it gently illuminates the surface of the waters, then mounts higher and writes upon the supple water. At last at its zenith it lights up a whole corridor of sea, a rich river of milk which, with the motion of the ship, flows inexhaustibly towards us through the dark ocean. Here is the faithful night, the cool night which I called for amid the noise of lights, drink and the tumult of desire.

We sail across spaces so vast they seem unending. Sun and moon rise and fall in turn, on the same thread of light and night. Days at sea, even and indistinguishable as happiness . . .

This life rebellious to forgetfulness, rebellious to memory, of which Stevenson speaks.

Dawn. We sail perpendicularly across the Tropic of Cancer, the waters groan and are convulsed. Day breaks over a surging sea, full of steel spangles. The sky is white with mist and heat, with a dead but unbearable glare, as if the sun had turned liquid in the thickness of the clouds, over the whole stretch of the celestial vault. A sick sky over a decomposing sea. As the day draws on, the heat grows in the white air. All day long the bow noses out clouds of flying fish, small iron birds, forcing them from their bushes in the waves.

In the afternoon we meet a steamer going back towards the towns. Our sirens exchange greetings in three great hoots, like prehistoric animals. Passengers lost at sea are warned that other men are present and exchange greetings with them, the two ships draw slowly farther apart upon the malevolent waters; all this fills the heart with sadness. What man who cherishes the sea and loneliness will ever stop himself from loving these obstinate madmen who, clinging to planks and tossed by the mane of immense oceans, chase after islands long adrift?

In the very midst of the Atlantic we bend beneath savage winds blowing endlessly from pole to pole. Each cry we utter is lost, flies off into limitless space. But this cry, carried day after day on the winds, will finally reach land at one of the flattened ends of the earth and echo timelessly against the frozen walls until a man, lost somewhere in his shell of snow, hears it and consents to smile with happiness.

I was half asleep in the early afternoon sun when a terrible noise awoke me. I saw the sun in the depths of the sea, the waves reigning in the surging heavens. Suddenly the sea was alight, the sun flowed in long icy draughts down my throat. Around me the sailors were laughing and crying. They loved one another, yet with no forgiveness. On that day I recognized the world for what it was, I consented that its good should also do evil and its drawback carry benefits. On that day I realized that there were two truths, of which one must never be told.

82   The curious Austral moon, slightly pared, accompanies us

for several nights and then slides rapidly from the sky down to the sea which swallows it. There remains the Southern Cross, the infrequent stars, the porous air. At the same instant, the wind also ceases completely. The sky rolls and pitches above our immobile masts. Engine dead, sails hove to, we whistle in the warm night while the water beats amicably against our sides. No commands, the machines are silent. Why indeed should we carry on and why should we return? Our cup runneth over, and a mute, invincible madness rocks us to sleep. A day comes like this which draws everything to a close; we must then let ourselves sink, like those who swim until exhausted. What do we accomplish? For ever, I have held it secret from myself. O bitter bed, princely couch, the crown lies at the bottom of the seas.

In the morning the lukewarm water foams gently under our propeller. We put on speed. Towards noon, travelling from distant continents, a herd of sea cows cross our path, overtake us and swim rhythmically northwards, followed by multicoloured birds which, from time to time, rest upon their horns. This rustling forest slowly vanishes on the horizon. A little later, the sea is covered over with strange, yellow flowers. Towards evening, for hour after hour, we are preceded by an invisible song. I go to sleep, at home.

All our sails stretched in a keen breeze, we race across a clear and rippling sea. At top speed our helm goes hard to port. And towards nightfall, correcting our course again, listing so far to starboard that our sails skim the water, we sail rapidly along the side of a southern continent which I recognize for having in former days flown blindly across it in the barbarous coffin of an aeroplane. I was an idle king and my chariot dawdled; I waited for the sea but it never came. The monster roared, took off from the guano fields of Peru, hurled itself above the beaches of the Pacific, flew over the fractured white vertebrae of the Andes and then above the herds of flies which cover the immense Argentinian plain, linked with one swoop the milk-flowing Uruguyan meadows to the black rivers of Venezuela, landed, roared again, quivered with greed at the sight of new empty spaces to devour, and yet never ceased failing to move forward or at least did so only with a convulsed, obstinate slowness, a fixed, weary and intoxicated energy. I felt then that I was dying in my metallic cell and dreamed of bloodshed and of orgies. Without space there is neither innocence nor liberty! When a man cannot breathe, prison means death or madness; what can he do there but kill and possess? Today, on the contrary, I have all the air I need, all our sails slap in the blue air, I am going to cry out with speed, we throw our sextants and compasses into the sea.

Under the imperious wind our sails are like iron. The coast drifts at full speed before our eyes, forests of royal coconut trees whose feet are bathed by emerald lagoons, a quiet bay, full of red sails, moonlit beaches. Great buildings loom up, already cracking under the pressure of the virgin forest which begins in the servants' courtyard; here and there a yellow ipeca or a tree with violet branches bursts through a window, Rio finally crumbles away behind us and the monkeys of Tijuca will laugh and gibber in the vegetation that has overgrown its new ruins. Still faster, along wide beaches where the waves spread out in sheaves of sand, still faster, where the Uruguyan sheep plunge into the sea and at once turn it yellow. Then on the Argentinian coast great crude piles of faggots, set up at regular intervals, raise slowly grilling halves of oxen to the sky. At night the ice from Tierra del Fuego comes and beats for hours against our hull; the ship barely loses speed and tacks about. In the morning the single wave of the Pacific, whose cold foam boils green and white for thousands of kilometres along the Chilean coast, slowly lifts us up and threatens to wreck us. The helm avoids it, overtakes the Kerguelen Islands. In the swedish evening the first Malayan ships come out to meet us.

'To sea! To sea!' shouted the magical boys in one of my childhood books. I have forgotten everything of the book except this cry. 'To sea!', and from across the Indian

Ocean to the banks of the Red Sea, where in the silent nights you can hear the stones in the desert, scorched in the daytime, cracking one by one, we come back to the antique sea in which all cries are hushed.

Finally one morning we drop anchor in a bay filled with a strange silence, beaconed with fixed sails. All we can see are a few sea birds quarrelling in the sky over scraps of reeds. We swim ashore to an empty beach; we spend all day swimming and drying ourselves in the sand. When evening comes, under a sky that turns green and fades into the distance, the sea, so calm already, becomes still more peaceful. Short waves blow a vaporous foam on to the lukewarm shore. The sea birds have disappeared. All that is left is a space, lying open to a motionless voyage.

The knowledge that certain nights of prolonged gentleness will return to the earth and sea when we have gone can indeed help us in our death. Vast sea, forever virgin and forever ploughed, my religion with the night! It washes and feeds us in its sterile furrows, frees us and holds us upright. Each wave brings its promise, always the same. What does the wave say? If I were to die, in the midst of cold mountains, unknown to the world, cast off by my own people, my strength at last exhausted, the sea would at the final moment flood into my cell, come to raise me above myself and help me die without hatred.

At midnight, alone on the shore. One moment more and then I shall set sail. The sky itself has weighed anchor, with all its stars, like those ships which at this very hour gleam throughout the world with all their lights and illuminate dark harbour waters. Space and silence weigh equally upon the heart. A sudden love, a great work, a decisive act, a thought which transfigures, all these at certain moments bring the same unbearable anxiety, linked with an irresistible charm. Is living like this in the delicious anguish of being, in exquisite proximity to a danger whose name we do not know, the same as rushing to our doom? Once again, without respite, let us go.

I have always felt that I was living on the high seas, threatened, at the heart of a royal happiness.

1953

PENGUIN 60s

MARTIN AMIS · *God's Dice*

HANS CHRISTIAN ANDERSEN · *The Emperor's New Clothes*

MARCUS AURELIUS · *Meditations*

JAMES BALDWIN · *Sonny's Blues*

AMBROSE BIERCE · *An Occurrence at Owl Creek Bridge*

DIRK BOGARDE · *From Le Pigeonnier*

WILLIAM BOYD · *Killing Lizards*

POPPY Z. BRITE · *His Mouth will Taste of Wormwood*

ITALO CALVINO · *Ten Italian Folktales*

ALBERT CAMUS · *Summer*

TRUMAN CAPOTE · *First and Last*

RAYMOND CHANDLER · *Goldfish*

ANTON CHEKHOV · *The Black Monk*

ROALD DAHL · *Lamb to the Slaughter*

ELIZABETH DAVID · *I'll be with You in the Squeezing of a Lemon*

N. J. DAWOOD (TRANS.) · *The Seven Voyages of Sindbad the Sailor*

ISAK DINESEN · *The Dreaming Child*

SIR ARTHUR CONAN DOYLE · *The Man with the Twisted Lip*

DICK FRANCIS · *Racing Classics*

SIGMUND FREUD · *Five Lectures on Psycho-Analysis*

KAHLIL GIBRAN · *Prophet, Madman, Wanderer*

STEPHEN JAY GOULD · *Adam's Navel*

ALASDAIR GRAY · *Five Letters from an Eastern Empire*

GRAHAM GREENE · *Under the Garden*

JAMES HERRIOT · *Seven Yorkshire Tales*

PATRICIA HIGHSMITH · *Little Tales of Misogyny*

M. R. JAMES AND R. L. STEVENSON · *The Haunted Dolls' House*

RUDYARD KIPLING · *Baa Baa, Black Sheep*

PENELOPE LIVELY · *A Long Night at Abu Simbel*

KATHERINE MANSFIELD · *The Escape*

PENGUIN 60s

READ MORE IN PENGUIN

For complete information about books available from Penguin and how to order them, please write to us at the appropriate address below. Please note that for copyright reasons the selection of books varies from country to country.

IN THE UNITED KINGDOM: Please write to *Dept. JC, Penguin Books Ltd, FREEPOST, West Drayton, Middlesex UB7 0BR*.
If you have any difficulty in obtaining a title, please send your order with the correct money, plus ten per cent for postage and packaging, to *PO Box No. 11, West Drayton, Middlesex UB7 0BR*.

IN THE UNITED STATES: Please write to *Consumer Sales, Penguin USA, P.O. Box 999, Dept. 17109, Bergenfield, New Jersey 07621-0120*. VISA and MasterCard holders call 1-800-253-6476 to order all Penguin titles.

IN CANADA: Please write to *Penguin Books Canada Ltd, 10 Alcorn Avenue, Suite 300, Toronto, Ontario M4V 3B2*.

IN AUSTRALIA: Please write to *Penguin Books Australia Ltd, P.O. Box 257, Ringwood, Victoria 3134*.

IN NEW ZEALAND: Please write to *Penguin Books (NZ) Ltd, Private Bag 102902, North Shore Mail Centre, Auckland 10*.

IN INDIA: Please write to *Penguin Books India Pvt Ltd, 706 Eros Apartments, 56 Nehru Place, New Delhi 110 019*.

IN THE NETHERLANDS: Please write to *Penguin Books Netherlands bv, Postbus 3507, NL-1001 AH Amsterdam*.

IN GERMANY: Please write to *Penguin Books Deutschland GmbH, Metzlerstrasse 26, 60594 Frankfurt am Main*.

IN SPAIN: Please write to *Penguin Books S. A., Bravo Murillo 19, 1o B, 28015 Madrid*.

IN ITALY: Please write to *Penguin Italia s.r.l., Via Felice Casati 20, I-20124 Milano*.

IN FRANCE: Please write to *Penguin France S. A., 17 rue Lejeune, F-31000 Toulouse*.

IN JAPAN: Please write to *Penguin Books Japan, Ishikiribashi Building, 2-5-4, Suido, Bunkyo-ku, Tokyo 112*.

IN GREECE: Please write to *Penguin Hellas Ltd, Dimocritou 3, GR-106 71 Athens*.

IN SOUTH AFRICA: Please write to *Longman Penguin Southern Africa (Pty) Ltd, Private Bag X08, Bertsham 2013*.